YOU'VE GOTTA BE JOKING!

by John Norment

Copyright © 1971 John Norment. All rights reserved. Published by Scholastic Book Services, a division of Scholastic Magazines, Inc.

1st printing ....September 1971

Printed in the U. S. A

FOR LAUGHERS ONLY

Mr. and Mrs. Appleby, vacationing in Rome, were being shown through the Colosseum.

"Now, this room," said the guide, "is where the slaves dressed to fight the lions."

"But how does one dress to fight lions?" inquired Mrs. Appleby.

"Very slow-w-w-w-w-ly," replied the guide.

"There's nothing like getting up at five in the morning, taking an ice-cold shower, and a five-mile jog before breakfast."

"How long have you been doing this?"

"I start tomorrow."

"Last night, by mistake, I drank a bottle of gold paint."

"How do you feel this morning?"

"Guilty."

"This shirt is too small for me. The collar is so tight I can hardly breathe."

"No, that shirt is all right. You've got your head through a button-hole."

"Did you see me come in the door?"

"Yes."

"You never saw me before in your life, did you?"

"No, I never did."

"Then how did you know it was me?"

You should always be kind to your friends, because if it weren't for them you'd be a total stranger.

Overheard in a movie house: "I'm so full of penicillin that if I sneeze, I'll probably cure everybody here."

Any recipe for a good speech calls for plenty of shortening.

Love is sometimes like a mushroom. You can't tell if it's the real thing until it's too late.

Always be sincere, whether you mean it or not.

Did you ever wonder what the speed of lightning would be if it didn't stop to zig-zag?

"I had my face lifted."

"Really, I don't see any difference."

"It fell again when I saw the bill."

A teacher was discussing one of her pupils.

"He has a mind like a blotter. He soaks up everything but he gets it all backwards."

The trouble with being a good sport is, you have to lose to prove it.

A salesman called a prospective customer, and the phone was answered by a small boy.

"Are your parents home?" the salesman asked.

The child said no and the salesman asked if there was anyone else there he could speak to.

"My sister," the boy replied.

"Let me speak to her then," the salesman said.

There was a long period of silence, and finally the boy returned to the phone.

"I'm sorry, sir, but I can't lift her out of her crib."

A leopard visited his optometrist to complain.

"Every time I look at my wife I see spots before my eyes."

"Well, what do you expect," scoffed the optometrist, "you're a leopard, aren't you?"

"Sure," conceded the leopard, "but my wife is a zebra."

"I'm sorry, but the lion is busy!"

"I just wrote probably the most beautiful poem ever written in the English language."

"Let me read it."

"Can't — I forgot to put paper in my typewriter."

A boy from New York was being led through the swamps of Georgia.

"Is it true," he asked, "that an alligator won't attack you if you carry a flashlight?"

"That depends," replied his guide, "on how fast you carry the flashlight."

If you can keep your head when all those about you are losing theirs — perhaps it's because you just don't understand the situation.

Customer: "I want a book called *The Red Ship* or *The Scarlet Cruiser* or something like that."

Clerk: "Here you are, sir, *The Rubaiyat*."

"All right, you!" screamed the mother pigeon to her backward squab. "Either you learn to fly today or I'll tie a rope around you and tow you."

"Oh, mother, not that!" cried her baby. "I'd rather die than be pigeon-towed."

"You promised we'd be home by five o'clock!"

You should try to put a little something away for a rainy day, even if it's only a pair of dry socks.

Teacher: "Why were you late this morning?"
Student: "I squeezed the toothpaste too hard, and it took me half an hour to get the paste back in the tube."

One good turn usually takes off all the covers.

What most people have ready for a rainy day is a washed car.

FOR BETTER OR VERSE

If I had a sense of humor
It would cut my woes in half
My trouble is — when trouble is
I just don't want to laugh.

It always make me laugh
So wonderful a treat
To see an athlete run a mile
And only move two feet.

'Twas the night before Christmas
And all through the house
Not a creature was stirring —
No spoons.

Jack Spratt could eat no fat
His wife could eat no lean
Separate frozen dinners they buy
And each feels peachy keen.

We water the lawn
To make it grow
Then when it does
We have to mow.

You plant a garden
You work like the dickens
Then what does it get you?
The neighbor's chickens.

What are little girls made of?
Stringy hair
And a look of shame
When caught in the rain
At a football game.

Brother Adam had his troubles
In bygone days of yore
But no one could say when he told a joke
"I've heard that one before."

Dressmakers jump
At Dame Fashion's command
And usually live
Off the fad of the land.

Mary had a little lamb
Freddie had a pup
Ronnie had a crocodile
And it ate the others up.

Dollar for dollar
Pound for pound
Money's nice
To have around.

Raymond's not a great fighter
He's very seldom a winner
He couldn't lick his fingers
After a chicken dinner.

If you can't tell vaseline from putty
Then there isn't any doubt
That sometime very soon now
Your windows will all fall out.

A conscience is a nuisance
'Cause it takes away the fun
You had in doing something
You shouldn't oughta done.

Doors marked "Pull"
Reduce the speed
Of folks who push
Before they read.

If you want to make hay
You just can't beat
The grass that grows
Under other people's feet.

This is the week for truthfulness
So I lay bare my chest
Of all my father's children
I like myself the best.

The crane with patience on one leg
Stands in a pond in the everglades
But he still gets enough to eat
For all things come to him who wades.

If you build a better mousetrap
And put it in your house
Before long Mother Nature
Will build a better mouse.

Opportunity knocks but once
Then comes again no more
Temptation bangs and pounds until
It smashes in your door.

Clocks for me
Hold very few charms
Especially those
With shrill alarms.

"Has a pair of stilts been turned in?"

EXTRA FUNNIES

The following is a letter received by the producers of a television quiz show:

"Gentlemen, I wonder if you'd be interested in having a contestant on your show who has sharp, pointed ears? Five of my ears have sharp points."

"Going somewhere?" inquired Freddie.

"Yes," replied Gladys, putting on her hat and gloves, "I'm going to the beauty parlor to get a finger wave."

"I wish you wouldn't bother," said Freddie. "I like your fingers just the way they are."

"Well, son, how did you do in school this year?"

"Fine, Dad, I made the football team."

"That's great," replied papa. "How did the team do this year?"

"Oh, we had an undefeated season."

"Remarkable."

"Yes," continued the son, "we didn't defeat a single team."

Excerpt from an essay by a third grader:
"I like trees because trees don't hit back."

Sign in a gift shop: "For the man who has everything — a calendar to remind him when his payments are due."

Dragon: "I'm stuck on this sword."
Knight: "So glad you like it."

An American was seated opposite a nice old lady in the compartment of an English railway train. For several minutes he chewed his gum in silence. Then the old lady leaned forward.

"It's nice of you to try and make conversation," she said, "but I must confess to you that I'm deaf as a post."

"How much do you charge for taking children's photographs?"
"Ten dollars a dozen."
"I'll come back in a couple of years. I only have ten now."

It seems a shame to repeat gossip, but what else can you do with it?

An Englishman was driving along a road in the United States, when he saw a large sign:

"Drive Slowly! This Means You!"

The Englishman stopped in surprise.

"My word!" he exclaimed. "How did they know I was here?"

One hippopotamus to another: "I had that dream again last night about playing concert piano."

No matter how flat your conversation is, some people like it even flatter.

A man walked into the railroad station.

"Is the train to New York on time?" he asked the ticket agent.

"Yep!" replied the agent.

The man sat down on the platform bench and waited. One hour passed . . . then two, and then three.

He went back in to see the station agent.

"I thought you said the train was on time," he said accusingly.

"Son," said the ticket agent softly, "I'm not paid to sit here and knock the railroad."

"Say, Dad, what do they call a Husky sled-dog when he's puny?"

Cowpoke: "Hey, you're putting your saddle on backwards!"

Tenderfoot: "How can you tell that, when you don't even know which way I'm going?"

"The reason I climb mountains is — because they are there!"

"That's the reason everybody else goes around them!"

Pam wore her beautiful new ring to school, but nobody seemed to notice it. Finally she said, "My goodness, it's hot in here. I think I'll take off my ring!"

A lady shopper approached a busy clerk.

"I want to buy a birthday present for my father," she said.

"Yes, ma'am," replied the clerk. "How about a nice tie?"

"No, he has a beard," the customer explained.

"Then how about a fancy vest?" the clerk suggested.

"No, it's a long beard," came the reply.

The clerk sighed, "Then how about some slippers?"

"Herman, your hair is getting thin."

"So who wants fat hair?"

"I don't suppose I could talk you
into being bait."

Tenderfoot: "Where's that horse you promised to sell me?"

Cowpoke: "He got better."

"Hey, you just gave me a nasty look!"

"You have a nasty look, all right, but I didn't give it to you."

Grandpa: "What do you want to be when you grow up, my boy?"

Small Sam: "I want to be a veterinarian, sir."

Grandpa: "Be a doctor instead. Animals don't have any money."

"Teacher?"

"Yes, Homer."

"Besides Washington and Lincoln, what other presidents were born on holidays?"

CROSS PATCHES

Of course you've heard about the mad scientist who:

Crossed a carrier pigeon with a woodpecker so when he delivers the message, he can knock on the door.

Crossed an octopus with a bale of straw and got a broom with eight handles.

Crossed a puppy with a chicken and got pooched eggs.

Crossed a highway with a bicycle and got run over.

Crossed a chicken with an army tank. Now the capons go rolling along.

Crossed a mink with a kangaroo, and got a fur coat with a pocket.

Crossed Metrecal with a bar of soap, and got a new shampoo for fat-heads.

Crossed a turkey with a centipede. On Thanksgiving, everybody got a drumstick.

Crossed a tiger with a watch dog, and got a very nervous postman.

Crossed an Idaho potato with a sponge. Got a potato that tastes awful, but it really sops up a lot of gravy.

Crossed a dance floor with a beautiful girl and got engaged.

"Eloise, who's that in there with you?"

GREAT GRINS

A Frenchman was relating his difficulty in trying to learn the English language.

He said: "When I first discovered that if I was quick, I was fast; that if I was tied, I was fast; if I spent too freely, I was fast; and that not to eat was to fast, I was discouraged. But when I came across the sentence, 'The first one won one one-dollar prize,' I gave up trying."

A traveling salesman lost his way and night was falling fast, so he asked a farmer if he could stay the night. The farmer thought it over for a while.

"You can stay the night on one condition," said the farmer. "Answer this question: Why does the chicken cross the road?"

"Excuse me," said the traveling salesman picking up his sample case. "I think I'm in the wrong joke!"

One of the greatest causes of world trouble is that ignorant people are so positive about things — and intelligent people are so full of doubts.

A small girl was explaining to her smaller brother that it was a sin to work on Sunday.

"Anybody who works on Sunday can never go to Heaven," she said.

"But what about policemen? They have to work on Sunday," he inquired. "Can't policemen go to heaven."

"Of course not," replied the sister. "They're not needed there."

A mathematics professor was complaining to the police because he had been knocked down by a hit-and-run driver.

"Did you get his license number?" a policeman asked.

"Well, not exactly," replied the professor, "but I do remember noticing that if it was doubled and then multiplied by itself, the square root of the product was the same as the original number, only with the integers reversed."

"Just look at all the presents my friend sent me from Florida — an alligator bill-fold, an alligator belt, and this beautiful pair of alligator shoes!"

"Your friend must be a philanthropist."

"Not at all — he's an alligator."

Teacher: "How do you spell Mississippi?"
Small Sam: "The river or the state?"

Science has now developed a new miracle drug which, when administered by a specialist under carefully controlled supervision, won't make the common cold any worse.

Mr. and Mrs. Stingerberry were having a discussion. "Now, look, Alice," he said — careful to keep his voice down so the little old lady sitting in the living room, knitting, wouldn't hear him. "I don't want to seem harsh, but your mother has been living with us for twenty years now. Don't you think it's about time she got a place of her own?"

Alice gasped in astonishment. "*My* mother," she said. "I thought she was *your* mother."

In spite of the long line in back of him, Small Sam stood in front of the ticket window and counted his change very carefully three times.

"What's the matter," the ticket seller asked, "isn't the change correct?"

"Yes, it's correct," replied Small Sam, "but just barely."

A cyclist stopped at a diner for refreshment. He was having a cup of coffee, and said to the man on the next stool, "I'm a little stiff from cycling."

"Is that so?" the fellow said. "I'm from Pittsburgh, myself."

27

There's one advantage in being poor — it's very inexpensive.

Money will buy a pretty dog but it won't buy the wag of its tail.

"I was in a dance contest last night and won first prize. Here's a picture of the girl, me, and the silver cup to prove it."

"Hey, that's not a girl, that's a kangaroo!"

"That explains everything, then. I thought we were jumping pretty high."

Worry is like a rocking chair. It gives you something to do but it doesn't get you any place.

What is so rare as the fellow who goes to the drive-in movie alone?

Why is it the loudest snorer is always the first one to get to sleep?

A hamburger by any other name costs a lot more.

"Beginner's luck!"

Some people hate to cook little link sausages because there's so little left after they've been thoroughly cleaned.

The new model Flurch is a good car for clumsy drivers because it has the fenders on the inside.

Two ladies went to see their first football game.

"I wonder," said the first, "why the coach puts all the big heavy men in the front line, and all the little thin ones behind?"

"Well," said the other, "maybe the coach used to work in a fruit store."

Doctor: "What seems to be your trouble?"

Patient: "Nothing. My family thought I should see you because I like cotton socks."

Doctor: "I like cotton socks myself."

Patient: "You do! How do you like yours — with oil and vinegar, or just a squeeze of lemon?"

"My uncle was arrested for feeding the squirrels at the zoo."

"How come?"

"He was feeding them to the lions."

Teacher: "What was George Washington famous for?"

Small Sam: "George Washington was chiefly famous for his memory."

Teacher: "What makes you think his memory was so great?"

Small Sam: "Because they erected a monument to Washington's memory."

The huge elephant looked down at the tiny mouse and trumpeted in disgust, "You are the puniest, the weakest, the most insignificant creature I have ever seen!"

"Would you mind writing that down for me," squeaked the mouse. "I want to use it on a flea I know."

If ants are such hard workers, how come they never miss a picnic?

Sunday School Teacher: "And what conclusions did you draw from the story of Jonah and the whale?"

Small Sam: "People make whales sick."

Geography Teacher: "Did you ever see the Catskill Mountains?"

Small Sam: "No, but I've seem them kill mice."

"I'm worried about my brother. All he wants to do is sit in his room all day and beat his drum."

"So, what's wrong with that?"

"From the inside?"

Small Sam was visiting the Modern Museum.

"What's that, Daddy?" asked Small Sam pointing at an abstract canvas.

"That's supposed to be a barn."

"Well then, why isn't it?"

"You really have to hand it to the Venus de Milo."

"How come?"

"How else can she eat?"

"My roommate makes life unbearable. He keeps six sheep and five goats in the bedroom and it smells terrible."

"Why don't you open the window?"

"What, and let all my pigeons escape?"

"He thinks he's a bird dog."

HOARSE LAUGHS

"Why don't you answer the phone?"
"It isn't ringing."
"Must you always wait till the last minute?"

"When you went to Disneyland, why didn't you take your little boy?"
"He didn't have any money."

Doctor: "When did you first suspect that there was something wrong with your anatomy?"
Patient: "It all began when I went into a hat store to buy myself a hat and the clerk told me I would need two."

All the world's a stage and it's certainly a popular show. In fact, some experts predict that before long there will be Standing Room Only.

If you want to catch a rabbit, all you have to do is hide behind a bush and make a noise like a carrot.

The local pharmacist persuaded Small Sam to stay in the store just in case the phone rang.

"I'll only be gone about ten minutes, just answer the phone and take any messages."

The telephone rang.

"Hello," said Small Sam.

"I'm calling to enquire if you have streptomycin and aureomycin — do you?"

Small Sam scratched his head, mused a moment, and then replied, "Madam, when I said hello, I told you all I know."

First Little Ink Drop: "Why are you crying so hard?"

Second Little Ink Drop: "I'm crying because my father is in the pen and I don't know how long the sentence will be."

"Instead of vegetables with the roast beef," said the customer to the waiter, "I'd like to make a phone call."

Being a candlemaker isn't such a bad job, if you don't mind working on wick-ends.

Remember the wods of the wise old man of the mountains: "If you can't win — don't lose!"

The quickest way to get a doctor is to turn on your TV set.

Customer: "Don't you think this steak you served me is a little thin?"

Waiter: "Don't be silly. If the steak was any thicker, you couldn't see the picture on your plate."

"What do you like best about gravy?"
"No bones."

Pianist: "I play by ear."
Companion: "I listen the same way."

A small dog moved into a neighborhood inhabited by championship caliber French poodles. Several of the poodles dropped by to welcome the newcomer to the neighborhood.

One of the poodles made the introductions. "I am Andre," he said with great dignity. "This is Henri, Pierre, and Antoine. Who are you?"

The new little dog smiled bravely and said, "My name is Fido."

"Fido?" howled all the poodles in chorus. "What a corny name! We can't associate with a dog named Fido!"

"I know," replied the little dog, "but just wait till you hear how I spell it . . . P-H-I-D-E-A-U-X!"

"Don't bother to wrap it—I'll eat it here."

There are so many medical shows on TV nowadays, the germs are beginning to demand equal time.

The good guys always win on every TV show except the evening news.

If you're thinking of gifts, why not give the "gift that keeps on giving" — a female kitten.

"How long will you be in that bathtub?"
"About five feet ten inches."

Soda water is a drink that tastes the way your foot feels when it has gone to sleep.

Movie Actress: "Remember, I am a star!"
Movie Director: "You'd look better if you were a little meteor."

"So you want to be a lifeguard, do you?"
"Yes, sir."
"How tall are you?"
"Six feet, eight inches, sir."
"Can you swim?"
"No, sir, but I'm a very good wader."

"What can I do to have soft beautiful hands?"
"Nothing. And continue doing it all day long."

Have you heard about the new soap they are putting out now? It's called Lumpo. Lumpo doesn't clean, doesn't lather, doesn't bubble. It just lies on the bottom of the tub and keeps you company.

"Why don't you play golf with Bill any more?"
"Would you play with a fellow who always cheats on his score, and moves the ball when you're not looking?"
"Indeed not!"
"Neither will Bill!"

The secret of bookkeeping is to stop lending them.

"Boboe is a science-fiction author. He writes stories about the planet Earth."

TYPOS, BLOOPERS, AND BONERS

Chris Rumpel suffered several broken and bruised legs last night when a sled on which he was riding struck a tree.

Troy (N.Y.) *Record*

Weather Forecast: Colder tonight. Saturday fair, probably followed by Sunday.

Mount Carmel (Pa.) *Item*

Miss Benson is in the hospital this morning after having been bitten by a spider in a bathing suit.

Mansfield (Ohio) *Tribune*

Not a single birth of any famous person has been recorded the past twelve months.

New York (N.Y.) *Times*

Miss Clifford is returning home by train as she gets seasick whenever she flies.

St. Louis (Mo.) *Post-Dispatch*

John Garber, 18, was accused of assaulting Larry Mullins, 16, during an argument with a package of frozen fish.

Jackson (Miss.) *News*

Boil one quart of water until tender.

Wilkes-Barre (Pa.) *Record*

Our brave pioneers worked with an axe in one hand, and a gun in the other, and a Bible in the other.

Atlanta (Ga.) *Bulletin*

Germans are so small that there may be as many as one billion, seven hundred million of them in a single drop of water.

Mobile (Ala.) *Press*

It is scandalous to see these society women going about with a poodle on the end of a string where a baby would be more fitting.

Chicago (Ill.) *News*

The principle effect of the storm was the moving of a lot of debris from where it was to where it is.

Dunbar (W. Va.) *Advance*

People searching for solitude are flocking here from all corners of the globe.

Cape Henry (N.C.) *Post*

Abraham Lincoln was born in a house which he helped his father to build.

Bainbridge (N.Y.) *News*

Miller's ice house caught fire and burned to the ground. With it 20,000 pounds of ice were reduced to ashes.

Peterboro (N.H.) *Transcript*

The Centerway lot will follow the pattern of other lots as far as parking fees are concerned. The meters will permit parking at twenty-five dents per hour.

Corning (N.Y.) *Leader*

She held out her hand and the young man took it and departed.

Boston (Mass.) *Transcript*

Miss Garrison, a senior at Alabama College, will graduate in June with a major in piano and a minor voice.

Montgomery (Ala.) *Journal*

It was Monday night and there were only three other people in the large dining room. Half of them were waiters.

Pasadena (Calif.) Independent

Contest rules are that snapshots must be of a person not larger than 8 x 10 inches.

Muskogee (Okla.) Times-Democrat

Valery is 17 and gives us nothing but hear-ache.

Lancaster (Pa.) New Era

Governor Gross said that this was his first visit to beautiful Lake Waramaug, but he hoped it would be his last.

New Milford (Conn.) News

Man was sent into this world to earn his living by the sweat of his brow. You didn't find Adam walking around the Garden of Eden with his hands in his pockets!

Cincinnati (Ohio) Bulletin

The game began promptly forty-five minutes late.

Cincinnati (Ohio) Enquirer

It won't be a real New England clam chowder unless you put your heart in it.

Boston (Mass.) *Traveler*

While the infield has made several improvements in the lineup, the outfield is still the shame that it was.

St. Louis (Mo.) *Post-Despatch*

While Gerry was running down the base line, the umpire kept a closed eye on the action.

Jackson (Mich.) *Citizen Patriot*

Police found the purple woman's bathing suit in a locker at the country club.

Van Buren (Ark.) *Press-Argus*

Charles Kirkpatrick is able to resume his studies after a siege of romantic fever.

Walla-Walla (Wash.) *Union-Bulletin*

"Give him a little more line, Henry."

WILD ONES

Some people thirst after fame and fortune, and some thirst after great wealth and power. But everybody thirsts after popcorn.

"How do you find yourself on these brisk wintry days?"

"I just throw back the covers and there I am!"

Mr. Stingerberry went running to his doctor with a badly upset stomach.

"What did you eat for lunch?" asked the doctor.

"For the first time in my life, I ate oysters."

"Were the oysters fresh?"

"How should I know?" said Mr. Stingerberry.

"Well," asked the doctor, "couldn't you tell when you removed the shells?"

"Maybe that accounts for it — I didn't know you were supposed to."

It's a sure sign a boy is growing up when he'd rather steal a kiss than second base.

You've heard about King Arthur and the Knights of the round table. Originally the table was square, but the knights kept sitting down with their swords on.

During the thirties the dust storms in parts of Oklahoma were so severe you could sometimes see prairie dogs digging holes fifty feet up in the air.

The man in the barber chair whispered, "Have you got another razor?"

"Why?" asked the barber.

"I'd like to defend myself."

"The fellow I used to work for is the politest man in the world."

"Why do you say that?"

"He sent me a telegram that reads, 'You're fired — best regards!' "

Two buzzards were floating along in the upper atmosphere almost motionless. Suddenly a jet plane went hurtling by, its exhaust belching fire and smoke.

"Wow!" said the first buzzard, "that bird was really in a hurry!"

"You'd be in a hurry, too, if your tail was on fire!"

People who live in glass houses might as well answer the doorbell.

Life is so complicated that by the time you find out what it's all about you've forgotten why you wanted to know.

Ronnie: "I've invented a new compass that always points the wrong way."

Pam: "What do you call it?"

Ronnie: "I call it a Tates compass, because he who has a Tates is lost."

A college education can't definitely guarantee you a job upon graduation, but it does give you four years to worry about it.

The following notice was found tacked on the student bulletin board: "Any boy finding a class ring with the initials L.V. on it is advised to return the ring immediately to Linda Vogelswinner or else he's going steady!"

Boss: "I hate to tell you, but your spelling is abominable."

Secretary: "Leave my stomach out of this."

Some people cause happiness wherever they go. Others whenever.

Small Sam's Aunt Jane was expecting a baby. "Your Aunt Jane," his mother said, "is going to have a baby, so you will have a little cousin."

Unimpressed by the news, Small Sam replied, "How can you tell it will be a cousin?"

Mr. Stingerberry climbed to the top of a flagpole and began singing at the top of his voice.

He was arrested and charged with disorderly conduct. After hearing the charge, the judge asked, "What do you have to say for yourself?"

"Well, it's like this, your honor, if I didn't do something crazy every once in a while I'd go nuts!"

Freddie: "I heard what you just said about me, and I'll give you just five seconds to apologize!"

"And what happens," demanded Ronnie, "if I don't apologize in five seconds?"

Freddie: "Well, how much time would you like?"

It's only human to have your mind wander. The trouble comes when you follow it.

There's a brief and magic moment at every summer camp. It comes at sunset during that brief moment when the flies have quit work for the day, and the mosquitoes haven't taken over.

The reason children are so happy is, they don't have any children of their own to worry about.

"My uncle caught one of the biggest fish ever caught in the state of Wisconsin."

"How big was it?"

"I don't know, but the photograph alone weighed nineteen pounds."

LOONEY LIMMERICKS

There once was a boy in Quebec
Who was buried in snow to his neck
When asked, "Are you friz?"
He replied, "Yes I is,
But we don't call this cold in Quebec."

A diner, while dining at Crewe,
Found a rather large mouse in his stew.
Said the waiter, "Don't shout
And wave it about,
Or the rest will be wanting one, too."

A glutton who came from the Rhine
When asked at what hour he would dine,
Replied, "At eleven,
At three, five, and seven
And eight, and a quarter past nine."

There's a stingy old miser who tries
All methods to e-con-omize
He said with a wink,
"I save gallons of ink
By simply not dotting my i's."

A mean old man of Tarentum
Gnashed his false teeth till he bent 'em.
When asked the cost
Of what he had lost,
He replied, "I don't know, I just rent 'em."

There was a young man from Japan
Whose limericks never would scan
When asked why it was,
He answered, "Because
I always try to get everything into the last
    line that I possibly can."

Fat Henry, from the Amazon
Put a nightie of his gramazon
The reason: That
He was too fat
To get his own pajamazon.

In New Orleans there dwelled a young Creole
Who when asked if her hair was all reole
Replied with a shrug
"Just give it a tug
And decide by how loudly I squeole."

There was an old man of St. Bees
Who was stung on the arm by a wasp
When asked, "Does it hurt?"
He replied, "No it doesn't,
I'm so glad it wasn't a hornet."

They tell of a hunter named Shepard
Who was eaten for lunch by a lephard
Said the lephard, "Egad!
You'd be tastier, lad,
If you had been salted and pephard."

There was a young girl in New York
Whose body was lighter than cork
She had to be fed
For six weeks upon lead
Before she went out for a walk.

No matter how grouchy you're feeling
You'll find a smile more or less healing
It grows in a wreath
All around the front teeth —
Thus preserving the face from congealing.

An oyster from Kalamazoo
Confessed he was feeling quite blue,
"For," he said, "as a rule,
When the weather turns cool,
I'm apt to get in a stew."

There was a young man from the city
Who thought a skunk was a kitty
To make sure of that
He gave it a pat.
They buried his clothes — what a pity.

A girl who weighed many an oz.
Used language I dare not pronoz.
For a fellow unkind
Pulled her chair out behind
Just to see (so he said) if she'd boz.

There was a young fellow named Fisher
Who was fishing for fish in a fissure,
When a cod with a grin
Pulled the fisherman in
Now they're fishing the fissure for Fisher.

"I give up. Junior. What has four
legs and flies?"

JEST IN FUN

The human brain is wonderful. It starts working the moment you awake in the morning, and doesn't stop until you are called on in class.

A tourist, driving along a country road, saw a farmer and his pretty little daughter sitting under a tree. The tourist stopped and admired the girl.

"What do you call her?" he asked the farmer.

"Amalysinita," the farmer replied.

"Isn't that rather a long name?"

The farmer gave the tourist a sour look. "Listen, son, we're not city folks — we've got time."

Once upon a time there lived a farmer who owned a big hayfield. The farmer's son decided to move to the city, and earn his living there. But when he got to the city the best he could do was a job as a bootblack at the railroad station. Now the farmer makes hay while the son shines.

Small Sam rushed off to school one morning without washing his face. When he sat at his desk, breakfast was still visible on his face.

His teacher, Miss Hansome, frowned and said, "Sam, why didn't you wash your face this morning? What would you say if I came to school with egg and jam all around my mouth?"

"Nothing," replied Small Sam, "I'd be too polite."

The ugliest man in the world went to a plastic surgeon to have his face lifted.

"I'll make you the handsomest man in the world," declared his doctor.

A date was made for the operation. Just before the patient went under the knife, his surgeon asked, "Now, do you want me to change your face completely?"

"No," answered his patient, "I want people to know who it is that looks so handsome."

He was so delighted with the restaurant that he returned the next day. This time they served him a very tiny steak. So he complained to the manager.

"When I dined here yesterday, you served me a steak twice as large as this one for the same price."

"Oh, yes," smiled the manager, "but yesterday you had a seat right in front of the window."

Small Sam's father took him to see a movie about ancient Rome. During the scene where the slaves were being thrown to the lions, Small Sam grabbed his father's arm tightly, and began to sob.

"Don't cry, it's just a picture."

"But, Dad, look at the little lion in the corner."

"I told you it's just a picture."

"But the little lion over in the corner," sobbed Small Sam, "he isn't getting any slaves to eat."

"I just returned from my vacation. I stayed at the Pleasant Arms hotel in Atlantic City."

"The Pleasant Arms hotel isn't in Atlantic City. It's in Philadelphia."

"In Philadelphia? No wonder it took me so long to walk to the beach."

Rain and sleet lashed at the windows of the old castle. The wind howled mournfully, and somewhere in the distance could be heard the rattling of chains.

"Has anything unusual ever happened in this castle?" the guest asked the sinister looking butler.

"Not for over forty years," croaked the butler.

Heaving a sigh of relief, the guest asked, "What happened then?"

The butler's eyes glittered with an ominous light as he hissed, "A man who spent the night here was still alive the next morning."

"...and then there's brie and camembert, cheddar and roquefort, swiss and gouda..."

Once upon a time there was a man who each day walked to work and passed a window where he saw a lady hitting a boy over the head with a loaf of bread. He decided it was none of his business, so he continued walking. He saw the same thing happen every morning for seven months. Then one morning he saw the lady throw an entire chocolate cake into the boy's face. Astonished, he peered into the open window and asked why.

"Oh," the lady said, "today's his birthday."

"I'll pay you a hundred dollars to do all my worrying for me."

"It's a deal. Where's the hundred?"

"That's your first worry."

"You see this bear on the floor," said the big game hunter. "I shot it when it was only five feet from me. It was a case of him or me."

"Well," yawned his unimpressed listener, "the bear certainly makes a better rug."

Good advice spied on the top of a mayonnaise jar: "Keep cool but don't freeze."

High-heel shoes were invented by a girl who had just been kissed on the forehead.

A baker went crazy trying to save money baking doughnuts. The larger he made the holes, the more dough it took to go around them.

Overheard in a Berlin Restaurant:
"Waiter, this sourkraut is not sour enough."
"It is noodles."
"For noodles, it is sour enough."

Television: A device that offers people who don't have anything to do a chance to watch people who can't do anything.

We'd have a lot less trouble in this country today if the Indians had only had stricter immigration laws.

Junior-high students in a Chicago school have christened one of their drinking fountains, "Old Faceful."

"Don't you know that if you eat too many candy bars you'll ruin your stomach?"
"That's all right, I always keep my coat buttoned."

Freddie Appelby was dining in a restaurant on a very tough steak. He jabbed and stabbed at it but couldn't cut it at all. Finally he called to the waiter.

"You'll have to take this steak back and bring me another. This one is so tough I can't even cut it."

The waiter bent over and examined the steak carefully.

"Sorry, sir, but I can't take this steak back now. You see, you've bent it rather badly."

"Hello, Small Sam, what did you study at school today?"

"Arithmetic."

"How much is one and one?"

"Oh," said Small Sam, "We didn't get that far yet."

A lonely stranger wandered into a restaurant in San Francisco.

"May I take your order?" inquired his pretty waitress.

"Yes," replied the stranger, "I'd like a couple of scrambled eggs and a few kind words."

Soon the waitress returned with his eggs and said, "Your eggs, sir. Will there be anything else?"

"Yes, what about my kind words?"

The waitress leaned over and whispered, "Don't eat the eggs."

Small Sam to parents bringing home triplets from the maternity hospital: "We'd better start phoning people right away, because they're going to be a lot harder to give away than kittens."

Song title: "I Can't Remember the Name I'm Trying To Forget."

Pamela: "Tell me what I have in my hand and I'll let you kiss me."
Ronnie: "A herd of elephants?"
Pamela: "That's close enough."

NOTIONS OF LAUGHTER

Don't bite the hand that feeds you because it's probably your own.

A student cashed a check for fifty dollars, and the cashier handed him fifty dollars in one dollar bills.

"Count it," said the cashier.

The student began to count and after he reached, "Twenty-four, twenty-five, twenty-six," he quit counting and said, "Sure, it's all here."

"What do you mean?" said the cashier, "You only counted about half of it."

"I know," replied the student, "But I figure if it's right that far, it's bound to be right all the way."

The old man of the mountains says that there are two kinds of women. There are the careless ones who lose their gloves, and the careful ones who only lose one glove.

Anybody who casts his friends aside like an old shoe is a heel without a sole.

"What's that piece of string tied around your finger for, Jerkins?"

"That's a knot. A forget-me-not is a flower. With flour you can make dough. Dough is money. I haven't any, will you lend me ten dollars?"

The eye doctor patiently tried lens after lens on an elderly lady who wanted to buy some glasses. Nothing seemed to bring things into focus for her.

"Now, don't get discouraged," the doctor told her. "It's not easy to get the correct glasses, you know."

"It certainly isn't," the lady replied, "especially when you're shopping for a friend."

"Do you have difficulty making up your mind?"

"Well, yes and no."

Once upon a time there was a poor family. They were so very poor that when Thanksgiving day came, they had to stuff their turkey with old newspapers.

If you were an automobile gas tank, would your needle be pointing to empty?

"I've just invented a shoe that has no sole, upper tongue, or lace."

"What do you call it?"

"Nothing."

"Is it bad luck to have a black cat follow you?"

"That depends, are you a man or a mouse?"

Simile: As nervous as an alligator in a handbag factory.

Advice to actors: A small role is better than a long loaf.

Some people put on weight only in certain places — pizza parlors, for instance.

Some people speak just as they think — only oftener.

Patience is all a worm needs to turn into a butterfly.

Announcer: "And now for all the news that happened during the last commercial. . . ."

How to dance the hula: First you put a crop of grass on one hip. Then you put a crop of grass on the other. Next, you rotate the crops.

Johnny Murray had always wanted to be a sailor, so on his eighteenth birthday, he enlisted.

His first letter home showed a certain amount of disappointment:

"Dear Mom, I joined the navy because I loved the way the ships were always kept so spick-and-span — but I never knew until this week who keeps them so spick-and-span. Love, Johnny."

They say the Navy has invented a new atomic submarine that will stay under water for four solid years — coming up just long enough to allow the crew to reenlist.

A man went to the best restaurant in town, ordered the finest dinner on the menu. When he finished eating, he called for the waiter.

"Do you remember how just a year ago I ate a meal just like the one I had tonight, and just because I couldn't pay for it, you had me thrown into the gutter like a common bum?"

"I'm very sorry about that," began the waiter.

"Quite all right," said the diner, "But I'm afraid I'll have to trouble you again."

At the state fair, they were choosing which bull would win the prize as grand champion. There were two perfect bulls in the contest. They were so evenly matched the judges found it impossible to decide which one was best. So they decided to let the son of the state governor pick the winner.

The governor's six-year-old son inspected the two bulls for a few minutes and then said, "I choose this one."

The crowd cheered the winner as the chairman hung the blue ribbon on it. Then the chairman leaned over and asked the governor's son, "Why did you choose the bull you did?"

The governor's son answered, "Because I think he'll give the most milk."

Two farmers were complaining about their bad crops.

"I've never seen hay grow so short in my entire life," said one.

"You think your hay was short," answered the other. "I had to lather mine to mow it."

Trader Benny: "When I was very young I was left an orphan."

Trader Horn: "What did you trade it for?"

Advice to summer campers in our national parks: Never pet a bear until it's a rug.

It's hard to be really mad at an alarm clock that doesn't ring.

Pastor Johnson: "Just think of it, Jonah spent three days in the belly of a whale."

Mrs. Abernathy: "That's nothing, my husband spent longer than that in the belly of an alligator."

Pastor Johnson: "Well, I declare — just how long was he in there?"

Mrs. Abernathy: "It's almost four years, now."

Ronnie (at the movies): "Can you see all right?"

Patricia: "Yes."

Ronnie: "Is there a draft on you?"

Patricia: "No."

Ronnie: "Is your seat comfortable?"

Patricia: "Yes."

Ronnie: "Mind changing places?"

One nice thing about money, the color never clashes with anything you're wearing.

"Don't bother to wrap it, I'll beat it here."

BEAUTIFUL SIGNERY

Sign in an Army Medical Center: "All Recruits Will Strip to the Waist. From Both Ends."

In an electric store window: "You phone us — We'll wire you!"

Sign in the window of a hardware store: "Five foot ladders, $12. Eight foot ladders — A little higher."

A clock store window has a sign reading: "There's no present like the time."

Sign on a Fortune Teller's door: "Medium prices!"

On side of a building: "Visit our bargain basement — one flight up."

A Chicago doctor hangs this sign on his door when he goes out to lunch: "Wrong Time — No See!"

Sign on a dentist's wall: "Be True to Your Teeth, Or They Will Be False to You."

Sign in the window of a Memphis book store: "Curdle up with a good murder mystery."

A restaurant window in Little Rock had a sign in the window reading: "Wanted — a man to wash dishes and two waitresses."

Sign posted along a lonely country road: "If you lived here, you'd be home now."

Sign by the flowers in Central Park: "Love 'em and leave 'em."

Sign in a Los Angeles USO: "Not responsible for dates left over ten minutes."

Slogan written on a bumper sticker: "No Comment!"

Sign on the lawn at a racetrack: "Don't step on the grass. It might be your supper."

In a midtown office building: "If you want to make ends meet — get off your own."

In the Merchandise Mart, Chicago: "Work as if your job depended on it — it does!"

Anti air pollution slogan: "On a clear day you can breathe forever."

In New York's Hayden Planetarium: "This way to the Solar System and the Ladies and Gentlemen's Rest Rooms."

On post office bulletin board: "To each his zone."

Name of a pet shop in Greenwich Village: "Fish and Cheeps."

Warning at a Maryland intersection: "Cross Road — Better Humor It."

At a Discount House: "Try our easy payment plan. One hundred percent down. Nothing else to pay."

Sign in an advertising agency: "Be origginal."

Sign in a Philadelphia nut shop: "If our nuts were any fresher, they'd be insulting."

The window of a second-hand store in California has a sign that reads: "We buy old furniture and junk. We sell rare antiques."

Sign on a Wisconsin filling station pump: "Cars washed. Compact cars washed and powdered."

In a car wash: "Batmobiles washed free."

There's a dress shop in Los Angeles called: "Have a Fit."

Sign in a Steakhouse: "Help relieve the coin shortage — tip heavily."

Name of a restaurant near the docks: "Buoys and Gulls."

Barbershop sign: "I need your head to run my business."

Advice on a beauty parlor wall: "Don't let your face be your chaperone."

Sign in a bookstore window: "You can't judge a book by its movie."

On a downtown loft building: "Wanted — woman to sew buttons on the fourth floor."

Department store: "Luxurious bath towels for the whole damp family."

Sign in a sportswear store: "Buy your girl a bikini — it's the least you can do for her."

Chalked on the sidewalk outside a public library: "Dr. Jekyll isn't himself today."

Outside a school: "Fite Illeteracy."

On a college wall: "Protest the rise of rebellion! Conform!"

In a furrier's window: "Be our Miss in Lynx."

Hair stylist's motto: "Dye now — gray later."

"You must have taken a wrong turn in
there somewhere."

FUNDAY FUNNIES

Friendly tip: You can keep your hair from falling out by knotting it on the inside.

A bird in the hand is useless when you want to blow your nose.

Rubbing hair restorer into your head regularly will give you hairy fingertips.

You can remove coffee stains from a silk dress with a pair of scissors.

Science tells us that a male moth can detect a female moth two and three-quarters miles away. No wonder we have so many moths to feed.

Gargling, first thing in the morning, is a very good way to find out if your neck leaks.

"My doctor gave me some pills to improve my memory."

"So?"

"I forgot to take them."

A rich gentleman, riding the train, was asked by the young man seated next to him what time it was.

"I won't tell you!" snapped the rich gentleman.

"Well, and why not?" inquired the young man.

"Because if I tell you what time it is, you'll start a conversation. You'll ask me what my business is, and I'll tell you. Then I'll have to ask yours, even though I'm not the least bit interested. Pretty soon we'll be right chummy. I'll get off at Sudbury, where I live, and you'll get off, too. My wife will be waiting for me in the car. I'll introduce you. My wife will invite you to come along to the house for tea. Then she'll invite you to stay for dinner and you'll accept. You'll meet my lovely daughter and fall in love with her. You'll probably propose and ask her to marry you. *And I don't want any man to marry my daughter who doesn't own a watch.*"

Experts agree that if your parents never had any children, chances are you won't have any either.

Mr. Appleby had a cat that loved to doze in the sunshine. Even when dozens of mice scampered all around him, the cat was completely unconcerned. So Mr. Appleby gave up and bought a mouse trap. The first thing he caught in it was his cat.

A man entered a pet shop and said he'd like to buy a parrot.

"I have a wonderful parrot for sale," exclaimed the proprietor. "There are twenty-three different colors in his wingspread. He can count up to a hundred and he sings like Paul McCartney."

"Never mind all that," interrupted the customer, "*is* he tender?"

The soil is so fertile in certain parts of Iowa, that the natives brag: "All you've got to do is plant a seed, spit on it — and duck!"

A new lighthouse was built along the rocky shores of northern Alaska. A couple of Eskimos were skeptical of the whole operation. Finally, one day after the lighthouse had begun to work, a heavy fog began rolling in. One Eskimo turned triumphantly to the other.

"See, it no work! Light shine. Bell ding-dong. Horn woo-woo, but fog come rolling in just the same."

"Isn't it disgusting the way some people drive? Just look at how close to us that lunatic ahead of us is driving."

The pilot of a new jet plane was flying over the Delaware water-gap. He pointed to a valley. "See that spot," he said to his copilot. "When I was a kid I used to sit on the bank fishing, and every time a plane flew by, I'd look up and dream I was piloting it. Now I look down and dream I'm fishing."

The man sitting next to Mr. Appleby on the train complained all the way into town. The awful service. The dirty cars. The senseless waiting, and the late arrivals.

"So all right, the railroad is really going to the dogs. Why don't you write a letter to your congressman?"

"That won't do any good," replied the complainer. "*I am* my congressman."

Science can put men on the moon, but it still can't explain why a woman's skirt sags while a man's shirt creeps up.

The best cure for insomnia is to just sleep it off.

"Doctor, for two weeks, every night I've dreamed that the most beautiful girl in the world was trying to kiss me, and I kept pushing her away."

"Well, what do you want me to do?"

"I want you to break my arms."

"Hey, let's sing a love song."

"O.K., let's sing, 'Hold That Tiger.'"

"But, 'Hold That Tiger' isn't a love song."

"It is to another tiger."

"Look at this masterpiece I just painted. What do you think I should get for it?"

"Six months."

"Is 'Ballpoint' really the name of your pig?"

"No. That's just his pen name."

Scientists are still debating whether or not splitting the atom was a wise crack.

What some people don't know about driving a car would fill a hospital.

Having thirteen people for lunch is bad luck — especially if you're paying the check.

Maybe your back sometimes feel stiff as a board because that is your lumbar region.

If you want to avoid catching cold, you should never drink out of damp glasses.

The three methods advocated for staying healthy are:
1. Eat what you don't want.
2. Drink what you don't like.
3. Do what you'd rather not.

Don't worry about headaches. They're all in your mind.

"Wrap it as a gift."

SMILE AWHILE

The champion prizefighter was beaten by a much smaller man.

"Why he only came up to your chin," said the manager.

"Yes," replied the champ, "but he came up to my chin one time too many."

"Did you do your good deed today, Tommy?"

"Yes, four other scouts and myself helped an old lady across the street."

"Did it take five of you just to help an old lady across the street?"

"Yes. She didn't want to go."

A sheriff, running for reelection, received only two votes, while his opponent received more than twelve thousand.

Even though defeated, the sheriff continued to wear two guns in his holsters.

A citizen told him, "You've no right to wear those guns. You've been defeated as sheriff."

"I know," replied the sheriff, "but anybody as unpopular as I am shouldn't walk around unprotected."

"How many slices of apple pie can you eat in one day?"

"Any given number."

Some banquet speakers are like the horns of a steer. A point here and a point there and a lot of bull in between.

Customer: "Is this tea I'm drinking? It tastes like kerosene."

Waiter: "Then it must be tea because our coffee tastes like turpentine."

An American was driving through the streets of London with an English friend. The Englishman said, "My windscreen needs a spot of cleaning."

"Wind*shield*," corrected the American. We invented the automobile so windshield must be correct."

"That's well put, old boy, but who invented the language?"

Billy, the fastest gun in the West, was brought before the judge in Pecos, accused of stealing a horse.

The frightened judge pronounced sentence, "You're an ornery horse thief and I give you just twenty-four years to get out of Texas."

Mr. Appleby returned home from a Miami Beach vacation and was telling a friend all about it. He wound up saying, "And they have wall-to-wall carpeting."

"New York hotels have wall-to-wall carpeting, too."

Mr. Appleby replied, "On the ceiling?"

"I represent the National Woolen Mills Institute. Could I interest you in some yarns?"

"Sure, go ahead. Let's hear a few."

Advertisement: "Lovely kitten desires employment as companion to small girl. Will also do light mouse work."

Doctors claim that cheerful people resist diseases much better than glum ones. So remember, "The surly bird always catches the germ."

An old grouch walked up to the ticket seller at the movies.

He stuck his nose through the little hole in the ticket window and sneered, "You advertise popular prices and yet you charge two dollars to get in. In the name of blazes, do you call that a popular price?"

"We like it," replied the cashier.

"Tell me, mister, where did you get that big 'O' on your sweater?"

"I played on the Northwestern football team."

"But Northwestern begins with an 'N'."

"I played on the second team."

Ronnie: "Where are you going?"

Tom: "For a walk around the park."

Ronnie: "Would you mind wearing my self-winding wrist watch? It needs the exercise."

"Waiter, will you bring me another sandwich, please."

"Will there be anything else?"

"Yes, a paperweight. My first sandwich blew away."

Two thoroughbred race horses were discussing life. The first horse was complaining, "Look how hard we work. Up at dawn for workouts. Run your legs off in a race, and if you lose, they make you work out twice as hard."

A stable dog interrupted saying, "What are you complaining about? Think of the poor milkman's horse, up at dawn and pulling a cart all day."

The second horse turned to the first horse and said, "Look, a talking dog!"

Mr. Twitchet arrived late for work one morning. He was bruised, had a black eye, his arm in a sling, and his clothes in tatters. His boss was furious.

"It's almost ten o'clock," screamed the boss, "and you were supposed to be here at nine. Where were you?"

"I fell out of a ten-story window," explained Mr. Twitchet.

"This took you a whole hour?" snorted the boss.

Pamela greeted Ronnie, "Notice anything different about me?"

"New dress?"

"No."

"New shoes?"

"No."

"New hairdo?"

"No, something else."

"I give up — what is it?"

"I'm wearing a gas mask."

Then there was the basketball player who was so dumb that when he got his letter somebody had to read it to him.

There are no statistics available at the present moment that show how many turtles have fallen in love with army helmets.

Shakespeare: "I've written a play about ancient Rome. I call it, *Julius Grab Her Quick Before She Runs and Gets Away.*"

Marlowe: "Your title's too long. Why don't you just call it, *Julius Caesar?*"

Waiter: "May I help you with your soup?"

Customer: "I don't need any help."

Waiter: "Sorry, from the noises you were making, I thought you wanted to be dragged ashore."

Old Pete Folderol was a very eccentric fisherman.

One day he was fishing his favorite pond when a friend stopped to watch.

"How long have you been fishing in this pond?'"

Pete turned, "I've been fishing here for ten years."

"But don't you know there are no fish in it?"

"Not at first I didn't," nodded Pete. "I guess I began to be suspicious about six years ago."

Pamela: "My, what artistic hands you have! What long sensitive fingers. Tell me, do you express any particular talent with them?"

Ronnie: "Well, I can tickle pretty good."

"There are only three things I can't remember. I can't remember names, I can't remember faces, and I can't remember what the third thing is."

This poem was written by a person who didn't like the weather in the state of Maine:
Dirty days hath September
April, June, and November
From January until May
It's pretty sure to rain each day.
All the rest have thirty-one
Without much chance of any sun
And if one of them had two and thirty
They'd be just as wet and twice as dirty.

A sign in a restaurant window reads: "T-Bone $1.00." The small print under that reads: "With meat — $4.00."

The editor of an Oklahoma newspaper printed a picture of a deserted farmhouse in an eroded field, and offered a prize for the best essay describing the picture. The prize was won by a little Indian boy:
"Picture show why white man crazy. Cut down trees. Make too big teepee. Plow hill. Water wash land away. Wind blow soil. Grass gone, people gone. Indian no plow land. Keep grass. Buffalo eat grass. Indian eat buffalo. Hide make teepee. All time eat. No work. White man heap crazy."

HO! HO! HO!

Then there was the sad tale of the optician who fell into the lens-grinding machine and made a spectacle of himself.

The swimming instructor at Camp Yokcho-kabodka was explaining the buddy system to his small charges. When finished he asked, "Now, can anyone explain what a buddy is?"

"Sure," replied Small Sam. "A buddy is someone who drowns with you."

There's another sad tale. This one is about the French-horn player whose toupeé fell into his horn — he spent the rest of the night blowing his top.

Grandmother: "Were you a good girl in church today, Susie?"

Susie: "Oh, yes, Grandmama! A nice man offered me a big plate full of money, but I said, 'No, thank you, sir.'"

Ronnie: "Why does a girl say she's been shopping when, actually, she hasn't bought a thing?"

Pam: "Why does a boy say he's been fishing when, actually, he hasn't caught a one?"

Absence makes the heart go wander.

Papa fly and his little boy were walking across the head of a bald-headed man.

Papa fly remarked to his offspring, "When I was your age, Junior, this was only a footpath."

We now have more food to eat than any other country in the world, and also more diets to keep us from eating it.

"How's your uncle doing with his new farm?"

"Not so good. There's not much money in milk and eggs anymore. So he sits up late every night trying to think of something else for the hens and cows to do."

A good excuse is one you can use over and over again.

Pam: "If you don't stop playing that saxophone this minute, you'll drive me stark raving crazy!"

Ronnie: "It's too late. I stopped over an hour ago."

A tom cat and a tabby were admiring each other underneath a romantic moon.

The tom leaned close and softly mewed, "I'd even die for you!"

The tabby gazed back at him with lowered eyelids and purred her reply, "How many times?"

Ronnie and Pam were watching television. The hero gathered the heroine into his arms and gave her a tender lingering kiss.

"If you'd kiss me once like that," sighed Pam, "I'd be yours for life!"

"Gosh," replied Ronnie, "thanks for the warning!"

Father: "Don't you remember that I promised you *no* spending money if you weren't a good boy, and you promised you'd be good?"

Small Sam: "Yes, Father, but since I broke my promise, surely you don't plan to keep yours?"

Tommy: "What's the best way to prevent infection caused by insect bites?"

Ronnie: "Don't bite any."

Pam: "If you put your hand in your pocket and found $7.86 there. Then put your hand in another pocket and found $419 there, what would you have?"

Ronnie: "I'd have somebody else's pants on."

A man was whipping his horse. A policeman warned him not to.

"Don't whip him, man — talk to him!"

The man turned to his horse, and by way of beginning the conversation, said, "I was born in the state of Michigan. Whereabouts do you come from?"

ONCE OVER LIGHTLY

Once upon a time there was a witch who decided to open a tea-room. She picked a good location and at first she prospered. Then she decided to cut corners and make some real money.

The witch found that if she saved used tea-bags and used them over again, no one seemed to notice. Before long the greedy old witch was using the same tea-bags over and over and over again.

First her business dwindled. Then it faltered, and soon she was bankrupt.

Moral: Honest tea is the best policy!

Junior, who had never spoken a word in all of his six years, finally blurted out at the breakfast table: "Mom, this toast is burnt!"

His amazed mother shrieked joyfully, hugged him and said: "Junior, why haven't you spoken to us before this?"

"Well," replied Junior, "up to now everything has been OK."

The small town bank installed a burglar alarm on the floor of the teller's cage. If a robbery occurred, all the girl teller had to do was press a pedal behind her foot, and this would ring a bell at police headquarters.

Several days after the alarm was installed a gunman poked a pistol at the teller and demanded the loot. The girl stepped back and stamped on the burglar alarm pedal. Several seconds passed in nervous silence. Then the telephone began ringing. As the girl reached over to answer it, the gunman grabbed it himself and lifted the receiver to hear an irate voice yell:

"Say, do you know you have your foot on the pedal that rings the alarm down here?"

Money travels so fast these days, the germs on it get air-sick.

Teacher: What letter comes after 'A'?
Small Sam: "All of them."

A moving-picture producer's daughter was asked to write a composition about a poor family. This was her opening sentence:

"Once upon a time there was a poor family. The mother was poor. The daddy was poor. The children were poor. The butler was poor. The chauffeur was poor. The maid was poor. The gardner was poor. Everybody was poor. . . ."

"Give me a definition of a tongue twister."

"Oh, that's when your tang gets all tongueled up."

A snail was climbing up an apple tree when a beetle spied him.

"Say," said the beetle, "there aren't any apples in that tree."

"I know," replied the snail, "but there will be by the time I get there."

Ghoul Kid: "Mommy, what's a werewolf?"

Ghoul Mother: "Shut up and comb your face!"

A famous newspaper columnist who writes about economics received a phone call the other day.

The voice on the other end of the line announced, "All this stuff you've been feeding the public about the high cost of living is ridiculous. My wife and I live happily, eating everything we like, on seventy-nine cents a week."

"Seventy-nine cents a week!" said the economics expert. "I can't believe it! Tell me how you do it — and to make sure I get all the details straight, please talk a little louder."

"I can't speak any louder," the voice said. "I'm a goldfish."

Ellen and Phil went for a walk in the country. Ellen saw some beautiful flowers behind a fence, and persuaded Phil to climb over and pick some for her.

After Phil had climbed over the fence, he noticed a bull standing a short distance away.

He called to a farmer in the next field, "Hey! Is this bull over here safe?"

The farmer replied, "Well, he's a heck of a lot safer than you are."

"Look out, Fred. Here he comes again!"

DIZZY DICTIONARY

Cartoon: A song sung in an automobile.

Flood: A river that's too big for its bridges.

Hypochondriac: Someone with a sick sense.

Butterfly: A worm who won his wings.

Eiffel Tower: French erector set that made good.

Dieting: The triumph of mind over platter.

Caterpillar: An upholstered worm.

Parent: The kin you love to touch.

Stowaway: The man on the ship who has the biggest appetite.

Scotland Yard: Three feet. The same as everywhere else.

Insulate: What you get if you stay out till all hours.

Autobiography: Life story of an automobile.

Latin Quarter: A Spanish twenty-five cent piece.

Coverage: To pretend to be older or younger than you are.

Missing: To sing incorrectly.

Net Income: The money a fisherman earns.

Unabridged: A river you have to wade across.

Snoring: Sheet music.

Conscience: What makes you worry about what it couldn't stop you from doing.

Diner: A chew-chew car.

Horse Sense: It's what tells you when to say "Neigh."

Bathing Beauty: A girl worth wading for.

Gossip: Rumortism.

Efficiency Expert: A man who waits to make up a foursome before going through a revolving door.

Hippopotamus: You already know what a hippopotamus is.

Authorship: A large seagoing vessel belonging to a writer.

Bee: An insect with a stinger three tenths of an inch long. The other eighteen inches is your imagination.

Paradox: Two medical doctors.

Boycott: Bed for a male child.

Pessimist: Someone who is only happy when he's miserable.

Golf Ball: A golf ball is a golf ball, no matter how you putt it.

Icy Remark: Froze prose.

Surfing: A tide ride.

Optimist: Someone who's thankful for the ventilation when he finds a hole in his pocket.

Cowardice: Yellow frozen water.

Red Light: The place where the hare and the tortoise meet once again.

Laugh: A smile that burst.

Egotist: Someone who's always me-deep in conversation.

Antique Shop: A junk store that has raised its prices.

Exclamation Point: A period that has blown its top.

Dictatorship: A form of government in which all that is not forbidden is compulsory.

Window Shopper: A store gazer.

Slogan: A revolver that shoots lazy bullets.

Mosquito: The original skin diver.

Jaywalking: Exercise that brings on that run down feeling.

Denial: A river in Egypt.

Hug: Energy that has gone to waist.

Hospital: A place where you live on needles and pills.

Frustration: What happens when a mosquito bites a turnip.

Theory: A hunch with a college education.

Diet: A penalty for exceeding the feed limit.

Inventory: The place where an inventor carries out his experiments.

Caution: A valuable asset when you're fishing, especially if you're the fish.

Vegetarian: A good salad citizen.

Restitution: An institution where you can go and get a good rest.

Duck: An animal that grows up when it grows down.

TALL STORIES
AND SHORT JOKES

Grandma: "Did you give the goldfish fresh water today?"

Small Sam: "Didn't have to. They never finished the water I gave them yesterday."

Mr. Stingerberry had been worrying about business. His doctor advised a long vacation. So Mr. Stingerberry decided to go away and forget everything.

On the first night of his vacation, as soon as he got in his hotel room, he opened his suitcase, and discovered, sure enough, he had forgotten everything.

Visitor: "You used to have two windmills here. Now, I see you only have one."

Farmer: "There was only wind enough for one so we took the other one down."

College Boy: "Hey, what are you doing wearing my raincoat?"

Room-mate: "You wouldn't want your best suit to get wet, would you?"

"I haven't had any sleep for nine days."

"That's terrible!"

"Fortunately, I don't have any trouble sleeping nights."

A small town is a place where everybody knows what everybody else is doing, but they read the local paper anyhow, to see who's been caught at it.

"I hear you got a dictionary for a birthday present. How do you like it?"

"It's interesting, but I wish it wouldn't change the subject quite so often."

When Captain Billy went to sea, his family kept a light burning in the window for twenty years.

When he finally returned home, his family gave him a royal welcome and an electric bill for $986.

Pam: "What did you get for your birthday?"

Ronnie: "I got this wonderful wool sweater."

Pam: "Oh, that isn't wool. It's plainly marked 'cotton'."

Ronnie: "Yes, I know — that's to fool the moths."

116

Ronnie: "When I arrived in this country, I didn't have a dime in my pockets. I didn't even have any pockets to put a dime in.

Tom: "How old were you?"

Ronnie: "I was born here."

Teacher: "When water becomes ice, what is the greatest change that takes place?"

Small Sam: "The price."

Tom: "That's a nice looking suit. How much did it cost?"

Ronnie: "Eighty dollars."

Tom: "Isn't that rather expensive?"

Ronnie: "Oh, I don't know, I got fifteen pairs of pants with it."

"What kind of work do you do?"

"I work for the Bureau of Internal Revenue."

"Doesn't everybody?"

The customer called the waiter over to his table.

"Why do you serve cloudy water in this restaurant?"

"There's not a thing wrong with that water," insisted the waiter. "The glass is dirty — that's all."

117

"What I hate about winter is, no picnics!"

A letter received by a congressman: "I write to you because I have nothing else to do, and I close because I have nothing else to say."

A fellow had his home right on the Russian-Polish border. He never knew whether he lived in Poland or Russia. The Geneva conference failed to solve his problem. Finally it was taken to the United Nations, where they told him his home was really in Poland.

"Hooray," he yelled, "now I won't have to live through another of those terrible Russian winters."

Two people were discussing a fat friend: "He's too big in the first place — and in the second place, too!"

"I see your cat came back."
"Yes, one day she wandered in, noticed we had an airconditioner and mice, so she decided to stay."

A New Yorker took his first trip out of town. He stopped for gas in a small town, got out of the car, stretched, took a deep breath and commented, "This is a pretty nice day for a town this size."

An internationally famous athlete in bed with a cold was told that he had a fever.

"How high is it?"

"A hundred and one," replied the doctor.

"And what's the world's record?"

Waiter: "Why are you washing your spoon in the finger bowl?"

Customer: "I don't want to get ice-cream all over my pocket."

Teacher: "What is the principle use for cowhide?"

Small Sam: "The principle use of cowhide is to hold the cow together."

The biggest strides toward safety in modern traffic are being made by the pedestrians with the longest legs.

If you'll just put off till tomorrow what you should have done today, maybe someone will invent a machine to do it for you.

Even a clock that doesn't run is still right twice a day.

Song title: "Everybody Has Someone. I've Only Got You.

A beggar stopped a rich man on the street.

"Believe me, sir, I haven't eaten anything in four days!"

Rich man: "You should *force* yourself to eat."

Small Sam: "Where are the Alps?"

Father: "Ask your mother. She puts everything away."

Mother firefly to father firefly: "I think our boy is very bright for his age."

Slip inside a Chinese fortune cookie: "Please ignore previous fortunes."

ODD ENDS

"I have over two hundred goldfish."

"Where do you keep them?"

"In the bathtub."

"What do you do when you want to take a bath?"

"I blindfold them."

Simple Simon decided to become a counterfeiter.

He printed some money and took it to the store. To test the money, he bought a dollar's worth of candy, and casually slapped a nineteen dollar bill on the counter.

The proprietor looked down at the bill, and then asked, "How do you want your change? Three sixes or two nines?"

Driving advice for long weekends: leave passing on curves to the beauty contest judges.

There's a new miracle drug that's so powerful, you have to be in perfect health to take it.

"There's really nothing to explain, officer.
We're on our way to a costume ball, that's all!"

Customer: "I'd like to buy some needles and pins."

Clerk: "Planning on doing some sewing?"

Customer: "Would you believe me if I told you I was a sword swallower on a diet?"

Small Sam drew a picture of a stagecoach, which was well done except it lacked wheels.

Teacher: "It's wonderful, Sam, but I don't see any wheels. What holds it up?"

Small Sam: "Bad men."

Strange how people who don't even know their next-door neighbors are curious about what's on the other side of the moon.

A Texan had a small farm with just a few sheep. One day his wife, while dyeing a bedspread a bright blue, had a little lamb fall into the bucket of dye. A passing motorist saw the lamb with the blue fleece and bought it for fifty dollars.

The Texan thought he might have a good thing going so he dyed some more lambs, and they sold at a large profit.

"Pretty soon," recalled the Texan, "I was dyeing them all colors — pink, yellow, lavender, green. And, you know, as fast as I dyed them they sold. Now, I'm the biggest lamb dyer in the whole state of Texas."

Singing is man's bathright.

Journalism Student: "Barbers make more money than some writers. I don't know whether to get a job in a barber shop or write a few novels."

Professor: "Why not toss a coin — heads or tales?"

Mr. Apricorn was rescued from being run over by a speeding automobile.

"Such heroism certainly deserves a reward," he said. He reached into his pocket and pulled out a large, live lobster. "Here, take this with my compliments."

His rescuer held the lobster out at arms length rather gingerly. "Well, thanks very much. I suppose I can take it home for dinner."

"No, no!" objected Mr. Apricorn. "He's already had his dinner. Take him to a movie!"

Traffic is getting so bad nowadays that if you give a man an inch he'll try to park his car in it.

Sherlock Holmes: "Egad, Watson, this is more serious than I thought. This window is broken on both sides."

A pedestrian was struck by a hit and run driver.

Policeman: "Did you get his license number?"

Pedestrian: "No, but I'd recognize his laugh any place."

He who laughs, lasts.

The boss was walking through the shipping room when he noticed a boy sitting on top of a large box and whistling.

Boss: "What's your salary, young man?"

Boy: "Thirty-five dollars a week, sir."

Boss: "Well, here's a week's pay. Get out. You're fired!"

When the boss saw his foreman a little later, he asked:

"How long was that boy with us?"

Foreman: "Why, he doesn't work here, sir. He was just delivering a package."

Mr. Stingerberry was telling a friend about the muscle-building course he was taking.

"I've been taking this course two years," Mr. Stingerberry told him. "Every week the postman brings me heavier weights and bigger equipment."

"But you don't look any stronger than you did before," commented the friend.

"I know," said Mr. Stingerberry, "but you ought to see my mailman!"

A mother's patience is like a tube of tooth-paste — it's never quite all gone.

"Ralph, why is an elephant gray?"

"I don't know, Ronnie. Why is an elephant gray?"

"To distinguish it from a blueberry."

When your outgo exceeds your income then your upkeep is your downfall.